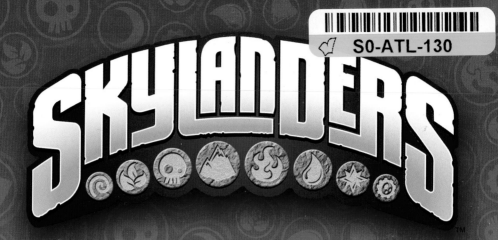

SKYLANDERS

RIFT INTO OVERDRIVE

Written by: *Ron Marz* & *David A. Rodriguez*
Art by: *Fico Ossio*
Colors by: *Ander Zarate*
Letters by: AW's *Deron Bennett* & *DC Hopkins*

ACTIVISION.

HC ISBN: 978-1-63140-412-2 | TPB ISBN: 978-1-63140-430-6   18 17 16 15   1 2 3

IDW
www.IDWPUBLISHING.com
IDW founded by Ted Adams, Alex Garner,
Kris Oprisko, and Robbie Robbins

Ted Adams, CEO & Publisher
Greg Goldstein, President & COO
Robbie Robbins, EVP/Sr. Graphic Artist
Chris Ryall, Chief Creative Officer/Editor-in-Chief
Matthew Ruzicka, CPA, Chief Financial Officer
Alan Payne, VP of Sales
Dirk Wood, VP of Marketing
Lorelei Bunjes, VP of Digital Services
Jeff Webber, VP of Digital Publishing & Business Development

Facebook: facebook.com/idwpublishing
Twitter: @idwpublishing
YouTube: youtube.com/idwpublishing
Tumblr: tumblr.idwpublishing.com
Instagram: instagram.com/idwpublishing

CHAPTER ONE

DROW WARRIORS?!

THIS IS THE PART WHERE YOU *SURRENDER*, SKYLANDERS.

OR *DON'T*. EITHER WAY, YOU'RE *DONE*.

ALL HAIL *EMPEROR KAOS!*

DON'T WORRY, GUYS, *I'LL* TAKE CARE OF THESE CREEPS.

MONKEY SEE, MONKEY...

FWAP

...DOOM?

WELL, *THAT'S* NEVER GOOD.

COME ON, SKYLANDERS, GET THESE CREEPY DROW *OFF* MY SHIP!

DON'T SAY WE DIDN'T GIVE YOU A *CHANCE*.

ENOUGH TALKING. IF THEY WILL NOT *BEND* TO THE WILL OF EMPEROR KAOS...

DON'T WORRY ABOUT OUR *DEFENSES*, SPYRO. THIS OLD NINJA COMMANDO HAS YOU COVERED, MILITARILY SPEAKING.

ALL THE *AIRSHIPS* HAVE BEEN SCRAMBLED...

"...SO WE HAVE A *DEFENSIVE BLOCKADE* AROUND THE ACADEMY.

"ANYONE WHO TRIES TO APPROACH WILL HAVE TO DEAL WITH *WASHBUCKLER*, AND HE'S ONE TOUGH OCTOPOD!

"WE'VE GOT A SQUAD OF *SHARPSHOOTERS* IN POSITION ON THE ACADEMY WALLS AND PARAPETS, READY TO OPEN FIRE.

"AND THE *CORE OF LIGHT* IS UNDER THE DIRECT PROTECTION OF OUR ENTIRE TEAM OF GIANTS. THEY WON'T *BUDGE* FROM THAT SPOT UNLESS *YOU* GIVE THE DIRECT ORDER.

"MIGHT SEEM LIKE A BIT OF *OVERKILL*..."

"...THEY SHOULD BE REACHING *KNOW-IT-ALL ISLAND* SOON."

HELLLOOOO!

THIS IS YOUR *CAPTAIN* SPEAKING. WE ARE BEGINNING OUR DESCENT INTO KNOW-IT-ALL ISLAND.

PLEASE REMEMBER ALL YOUR CARRY-ON ITEMS, AND THANK YOU FOR FLYING WITH THE OL' *FLYNNSTER.*

THE *LAST* TIME WE CAME HERE, THE PLACE WAS OVERRUN WITH *TROLLS.* YOU GUYS *TOOK CARE* OF THAT, RIGHT?

OF COURSE, BUT I WOULD STILL RECOMMEND YOU STAY *ALERT* AND READY FOR ANYTHING.

HEY, *NO PROBLEMO!* "READY FOR ANYTHING" IS TOTALLY MY *JAM!*

EVERYTHING LOOKS *CLEAR.*

LET'S TRACK DOWN THOSE *STONEHEADS.*

YOU KNOW, LOOKS LIKE YOU GUYS HAVE ALL THIS *UNDER CONTROL.* MAYBE I SHOULD STAY BACK HERE WITH MY SHIP AND STAND GUARD? OR SOMETHING?

DO WHAT YOU WANT, FLYNN, BUT KEEP IT *DOWN.* IF SOMEONE'S *HERE,* YOU'RE GOING TO LEAD THEM RIGHT TO US!

HARK! WHO GOES THERE?!

WAIT, DON'T TELL ME, I DON'T WANT TO KNOW!

KAOS HAS WOKEN A POWER LONG *HIDDEN*, CONSUMING ALL MAGIC THROUGH WAYS MOST *FORBIDDEN*.

A TERRIBLE THREAT TO ALL WHO WALK, SWIM OR *FLY*, MAKING TRAVEL IMPOSSIBLE THROUGH PORTAL OR *SKY*.

IT'S *WORSE* THAN WE THOUGHT.

WE'RE LOOKING FOR THE MYTHICAL *RIFT ENGINES*. WILL THEY BE ABLE TO *HELP* US?

THE RIFT ENGINES WERE MADE BY THE ANCIENTS TO *SPREAD* MAGIC AND LIGHT TO WORLDS YET *UNTREAD*.

THEIR POWER IS VAST AND CANNOT BE *DENIED*. YOU'LL CREATE RIFTS AND RIDE WORMHOLES, AND PERHAPS TURN THE *TIDE*.

DID IT JUST SAY THE ANCIENTS USED RIFT ENGINES TO CONNECT SKYLANDS TO *EVERYTHING?!*

IT *TOTALLY* DID. YOU GUYS THINK THAT'LL DO THE *TRICK?*

WE'D BETTER *HOPE* SO! WHERE CAN WE *FIND* THESE RIFT ENGINES?

HA HA HA HA HA

AW, MAN, I *KNOW* THAT LAUGH.

LET'S NOT *PANIC* YET. MAYBE HE'S JUST HERE TO GIVE YOU THAT *FIVE BUCKS* HE OWES YOU.

KRAKLE

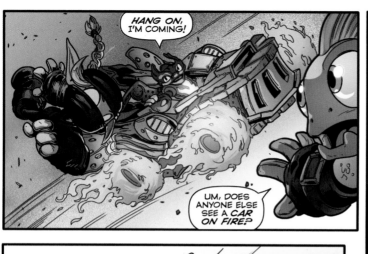

HEY, EVERYONE! I DID IT, I'M *BACK!*

AND LOOK WHO I *BROUGHT!*

WE ALMOST GOT *EATEN* BY ONE OF THOSE RIFTS, AND THEN, THIS *FIRE CAR* CAME *VROOOOMING* OUTTA NOWHERE, AND THEN THIS *SHINY JET* WENT *WHOOSH,* AND THEY TOTALLY *SAVED* US!

WELL, THAT'S *WONDERFUL,* BLOBBERS. BUT WHO ARE *THEY?*

WE'RE HAPPY TO MEET *ALL* OF YOU.

I'M *SPITFIRE,* THE FASTEST DRIVER IN THE *SUPER SKYLANDS RACING CIRCUIT.* OR, I *WOULD* HAVE BEEN, IF THE RACES HADN'T BEEN CANCELED DUE TO A SUDDEN GUST OF KAOS.

SINCE THEN, I'VE BEEN OUTRUNNING THESE CRAZY *RIFTS.* THAT'S HOW I MET MY PAL *STORMBLADE.*

I'VE BEEN TO ONE END OF SKYLANDS AND BACK IN MY *SKY SLICER,* AND I'VE *NEVER* SEEN ANYTHING LIKE THIS!

AFTER SPITFIRE AND I HELPED EVACUATE THE *STORMY STRONGHOLD,* THE ROYAL FAMILY SAID THE *STONEHEADS* MIGHT KNOW WHAT'S CAUSING THE RIFTS.

SO WE GOT THE *OTHERS* TOGETHER AND CAME LOOKING FOR ANSWERS!

OTHERS?

WHAT OTHERS?

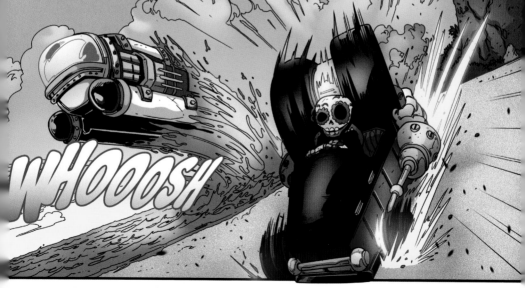

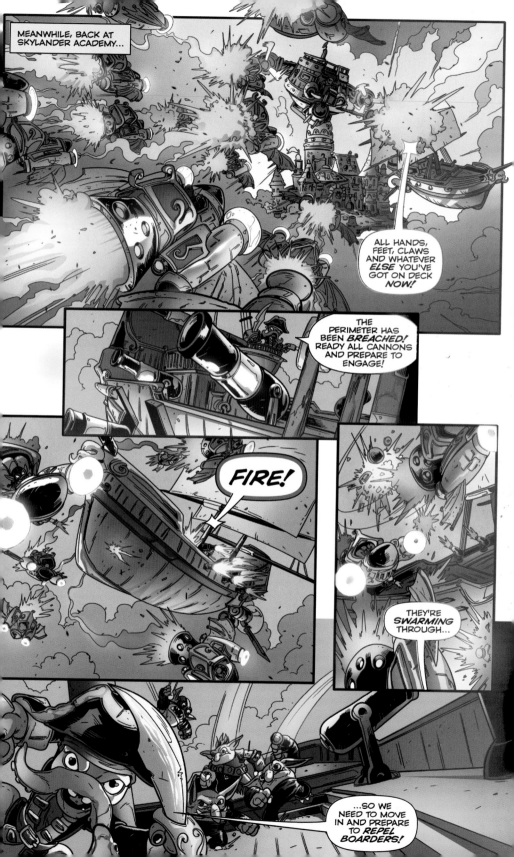

CHAPTER THREE

NOT THAT I MIND TAKING THE SCENIC ROUTE, BUT WE'LL NEED A *DESTINATION* AT SOME POINT.

THE STONEHEAD DIDN'T GIVE US MUCH TO WORK WITH.

ALL IT SAID WAS "THERE'S AN EYE OF A STORM RAGING ABOVE AND *BELOW*; A PATHWAY OF WHIRLS LEADING TO THE CITY OF *WOE*."

UGH, IT *WOULD* RHYME. WHY CAN'T THOSE THINGS EVER SPEAK IN CLEAR SENTENCES?

WAIT, SAY THAT *LAST PART* AGAIN!

"THERE'S AN EYE OF A STORM RAGING ABOVE AND *BELOW*; A PATHWAY OF WHIRLS LEADING TO THE CITY OF *WOE*."

THAT'S *IT!* I KNOW THE *ANSWER*...

"...I KNOW WHERE WE HAVE TO *GO!*"

WELCOME, EVERYONE, TO THE *WHIRLPOOL OF DESTINY.*

TO BE CONTINUED IN SKYLANDERS: SUPERCHARGERS!

SPITFIRE

BIO

Spitfire was on pace to become the fastest driver in the Super Skylands Racing Circuit. With his lightning-quick reflexes and nerves of steel, this tech-enhanced flame spirit was absolutely unbeatable. But during the championship event at Skywinder Canyon, he was illegally bumped off course by a goblin racer and sent flying into the canyon wall in a fiery explosion! Most thought that this would put an end to his racing career. But three weeks later, he was back on the track, more fired up than ever t claim the title. Unfortunately, it was then that all of Skylands fell under the rule of Kaos in his Sky Eating machine, and the racing came to an end. That's when Spitfire was approached by Master Eon with an offer that could get him back behind the wheel as the new leader of an elite driving team— the Skylander SuperChargers!

STORMBLADE

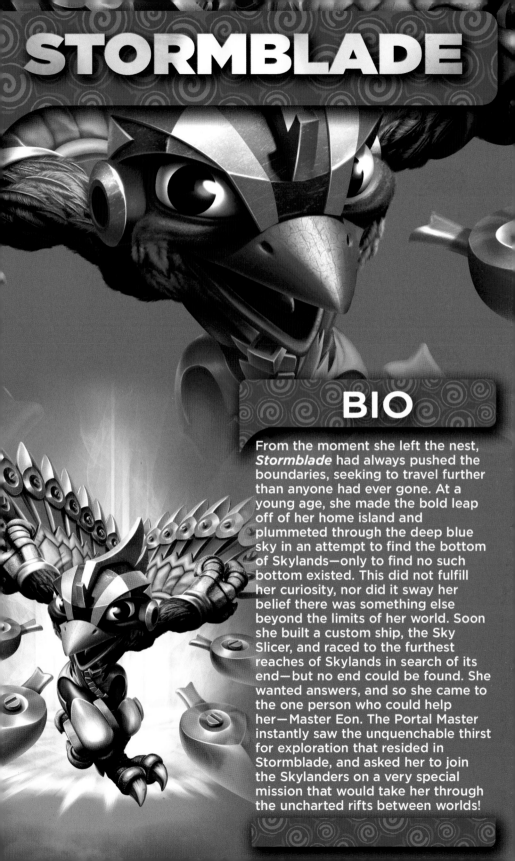

BIO

From the moment she left the nest, *Stormblade* had always pushed the boundaries, seeking to travel further than anyone had ever gone. At a young age, she made the bold leap off of her home island and plummeted through the deep blue sky in an attempt to find the bottom of Skylands—only to find no such bottom existed. This did not fulfill her curiosity, nor did it sway her belief there was something else beyond the limits of her world. Soon she built a custom ship, the Sky Slicer, and raced to the furthest reaches of Skylands in search of its end—but no end could be found. She wanted answers, and so she came to the one person who could help her—Master Eon. The Portal Master instantly saw the unquenchable thirst for exploration that resided in Stormblade, and asked her to join the Skylanders on a very special mission that would take her through the uncharted rifts between worlds!

FIESTA

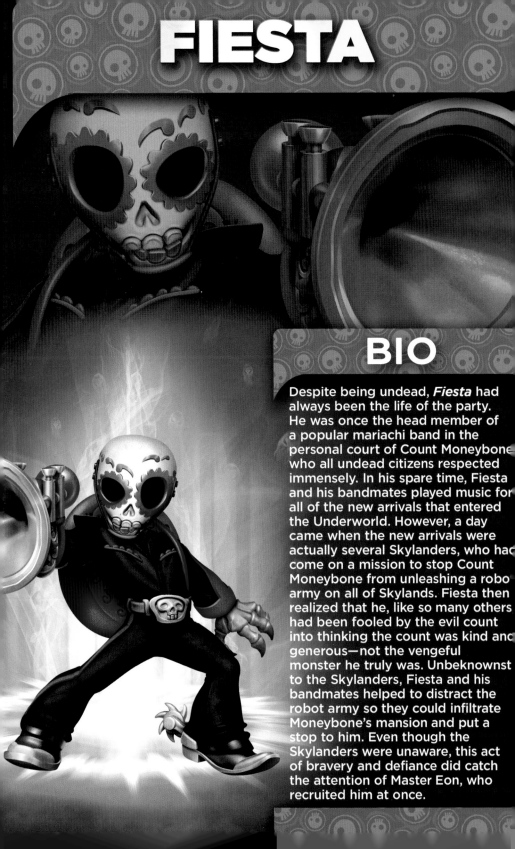

BIO

Despite being undead, *Fiesta* had always been the life of the party. He was once the head member of a popular mariachi band in the personal court of Count Moneybone who all undead citizens respected immensely. In his spare time, Fiesta and his bandmates played music for all of the new arrivals that entered the Underworld. However, a day came when the new arrivals were actually several Skylanders, who had come on a mission to stop Count Moneybone from unleashing a robo army on all of Skylands. Fiesta then realized that he, like so many others had been fooled by the evil count into thinking the count was kind and generous—not the vengeful monster he truly was. Unbeknownst to the Skylanders, Fiesta and his bandmates helped to distract the robot army so they could infiltrate Moneybone's mansion and put a stop to him. Even though the Skylanders were unaware, this act of bravery and defiance did catch the attention of Master Eon, who recruited him at once.

SMASH HIT

BIO

Smash Hit came from a long line of Warsupials—a rare species widely renowned for their skills in combat. But in more peaceful times, his people were responsible for locating and demolishing any remaining artifacts from the Arkeyan Empire that were deemed too dangerous to leave standing. Smash Hit liked his job because it allowed him to do what he loved most—break things! He was so skillful with his wrecking ball that he could single-handedly dismantle an entire Arkeyan Conquertron in under an hour and still have time for a snack. When Master Eon noticed his skill, he enlisted the talented Warsupial into a new wrecking crew he was forming to take on Kaos—the SuperChargers!

DIVE-CLOPS

BIO

Believe it or not, *Dive-Clops* is actually the twin brother of Eye-Brawl. When he was young, his batwings were blasted off by pirates while flying over the Swirling Sea, causing him to plunge into the abyss below. After rolling on the bottom for several days, he was discovered by an underwater civilization of Jelly Dwarves. They were instantly fascinated by the bizarre-looking eyeball and took him back to their Corral Castle, where they built him a magnificent dive suit that would allow him to explore the depths of the sea. But everything changed when Dive-Clops decided to venture to the mysterious Whirlpool of Destiny deep within the ocean. As he got closer, he suddenly felt pulled by its immense power, and reemerged to discover that thousands of years had passed! Now with his destiny before him as a member of the Skylanders, Dive-Clops lets the minions of Kaos know that there are many dangers of the deep!

HIGH VOLT

BIO

High Volt was once the commander of a special security force that was in charge of patrolling the border between the known regions of Skylands and the mysterious uncharted region known as the Outlands. From atop the Shockspire Tower, their security headquarters, High Volt vigilantly monitored any strange activity beyond the border, knowing that Kaos and his minions were always up to no good. Over the years, he had defended Skylands against countless Greeble attacks, Troll uprisings, and even a few evil food chains that were attempting to expand. But on a recent patrol mission into the Outlands, High Volt discovered a heavily guarded construction site, where Kaos' minions appeared to be building a colossal Doom Station of Ultimate Destruction! Realizing at once that all of Skylands was in danger, he raced to the Skylanders Academy to inform Master Eon and joined the Skylanders in their fight to stop it!

SPLAT

BIO

Splat grew up in a typical faun village, which was perfectly manicured and orderly. Every day in school, she and her classmates would recite the same poems, play the same music, and paint the same picture—which was always a portrait of their great ancestor, Fluty Hoofdancer. But this didn't suit Splat. The only art she wanted to learn was the art of war! After school, she would sneak off to the river and practice her own free-form fighting technique against Chompies and other creatures that were causing trouble. When the elder fauns learned of this, they were outraged. But soon thereafter, a band of Drow attacked the village to steal their valuable art, and while the other fauns cowered in fear, Splat stood her ground. Unleashing her self-taught fighting style, she defended her village and sent the Drow running. Now, as a member of the Skylanders, Splat makes quite the impression wherever she goes!

THRILLIPEDE

BIO

Thrillipede served in the Millipede Military in the outer regions of Skylands. As the top pilot in his unit, Thrillipede was responsible for single-handedly blasting over 300 Greeble warships out of the sky! When the Great Greeble War came to an end, he returned to his hometown of Flutter Bay as a celebrated hero. He was the talk of the town and everyone wanted to shake the many hands of the famous young pilot. News of his heroics eventually made their way to Captain Flynn at the Skylander Academy, who set out to determine if the stories were true. In a series of friendly challenges, the two pilots raced, soared through obstacles, and performed incredible stunts in front of a cheering Flutter Bay crowd. In each event, Thrillipede stood victorious, and was asked to join the Skylanders shortly after. Of course, Flynn later admitted that he "let him win" so that Thrillipede wouldn't be embarrassed in front of his hometown.

SKLYLANDERS™
THE KAOS TRAP

ISBN: 978-1-63140-141-1

SKLYLANDERS™
CHAMPIONS

ISBN: 978-1-63140-229-6

SKLYLANDERS™
RETURN OF THE
DRAGON KING

ISBN: 978-1-63140-268-5

IDW

WWW.IDWPUBLISHING.C
© 2015 Activision Publishing, Inc. TM
trademark, SM is a service mark, and ACTIVISI
a registered trademark of Activision Publishin